ANCHOR
BOOKS

A WALK IN THE PARK

Edited by

Sarah Marshall

First published in Great Britain in 2003 by
ANCHOR BOOKS
Remus House,
Coltsfoot Drive,
Peterborough, PE2 9JX
Telephone (01733) 898102

SB ISBN 1 84418 267 3

FOREWORD

Anchor Books is a small press, established in 1992, with the aim of promoting readable poetry to as wide an audience as possible.

We hope to establish an outlet for writers of poetry who may have struggled to see their work in print.

The poems presented here have been selected from many entries, and as always editing proved to be a difficult task.

I trust this selection will delight and please the authors and all those who enjoy reading poetry.

Sarah Marshall
Editor

CONTENTS

PERCY PENGUIN

Little Percy penguin was putting on some weight -
But the hungrier he felt – the more he ate!
He was a little worried and he said, 'I wish
I didn't get so hungry, or eat so many fish.'
His playmate Peter pelican said, 'If you don't stop soon,
You're going to end up looking like a great, big, fat balloon.'
Enormous Ernie elephant was laughing, full of glee,
'You'd better watch it Percy - or you'll finish up like me.'
Georgie the giraffe was looking over a high wall
Saying, 'See what I can do, I'm not fat, I'm tall.'
Little Percy waddled off home in time for dinner.
He'd go and see what Mum could do to help to make him thinner.
His mum threw back her head and laughed, 'You are a silly pup -
You're not growing fat my boy - you're just growing up!'

Nancy McKillops

RUDOLPH THE RED-NOSED LIAR

Rudolph the red-nosed reindeer
Has a very shiny nose
And like young Pinocchio
When he tells a fib it grows.

So if on Christmas Eve
You see a bright light in the sky,
You'll know that naughty Rudolph
Has told a great big lie.

Joyce Walker

THE CAT NEXT DOOR

There's a cat next door who's tall and fat,
I think he's eaten a seven foot rat.
He called in to see me a week last May
And asked if he could borrow my car for the day.
I said, 'Cats can't drive.' He replied, 'Well that's true,
But I've been taking lessons from a kangaroo.'

Ray Westlake

FLOWERS FOR THE CHILDREN

The golden flowers that herald spring
gleam in the March and April sun:
aconite, coltsfoot, daffodil -
treasures of great Hyperion -
and little varnished celandine,
spill from the store where riches shine.

But May comes dressed in virgin white,
carpets of daisies laid to tread,
with blossoms in her flowing hair
and gardens' summer snowflake spread;
the last narcissus' golden eye
watches the bridal month go by.

Against the blue, tall whitebells stir,
small stitchwort weaves a worthy gown;
along the lanes, most daintily,
a veil of Queen Anne's lace hangs down;
Jack-by-the-hedge stands tall and bright
to welcome May, the year's delight.

Leonora Slinn

SMILING CHILD

What joy and elation a smiling child can bring
To some old soul in sickness and stress.
That smile of endearment lifts one's heart
And makes a brighter day.
Their shouts of glee, clambering on your knee.
The loving cuddles, kisses of love.
Goodness in its wee heart.
Yet comes the day, we must part.
The final I love you, see you when I return.
Goodbye, God bless.
Ah, go on then, one more kiss.

Nancy Elliott

IT'S TIME FOR BED

Finally, it's time for bed.
Although I have tried
to stop the truth.
It's time to stop from
being loud.

I don't want to go up.
I wish it was the start
of the morning again.
But it's no use
and I am so tired.

Kirk Antony Watson

A LAUGH IN SCHOOL

I had a laugh in school today, it was really funny.
I rather thought I might, cos I had a dickey tummy.
When I was sitting in class and trying to get on with my work,
I thought, *it's only a matter of time*, cos my tummy was going berserk.
Without any effort a steaming boff shot from my bum,
It took about four seconds for the whole room to hum.
Then came the next one, it rippled down my legs.
That one was disgusting, and smelt like rotten eggs.
Everyone in class shouted, 'Erh, what's that smell?'
I cracked on I didn't know and said, 'I can smell it as well.'
The third trump was brewing, oh and then it really let rip,
Then everyone knew it was me, it sounded like a foghorn on a ship.
'I think I need to go, Miss please can I go to the loo?'
'Yes and make it quick, don't you dare follow through!'

Karon Crocombe

LITTLE USE!

Little Miss Muffett sat on a tuffet,
Eating her strawberries and cream,
There came a big spider that sat down beside her,
Hoping that it had not been seen.
Little Miss Good Manner picked up a spanner,
Used it like a hammer,
The poor spider was suddenly a 'has been'.
That little darling began belly-laughing,
She had lost all her fears far away,
In came her mother, with kisses did smother,
Looked at the spanner and started to pray.
In came her daddy who got into a paddy
And started his cursing again,
Had searched for that spanner,
Raised his hand then to tan her,
Lashed out and gave her some pain.

Therein a lesson, best make a confession,
State what you are feeling instead.
Don't use my spanner, go find a hammer,
As that is one thing that will not lose its head
Stifle that temper, that's the way to help her,
Explain how simple it is to be calm.
Do not hit one another, like I've hit your mother,
As receiving a black eye does one much harm.
Don't be like Miss Muffet, trying to 'tough it',
Be someone nicer by half
Be a bit nicer, a good-natured lifer,
Don't be bad humoured, just laugh,
You will find life better, undo the fetter,
You'll earn much praise from above,
Off hate be shrugging, try a little more hugging,
The world will be far nicer with love.

Jon El Wright

THE SUIT OF ARMOUR

Alone the suit of armour sits,
Upon his noble steed.
Tied up in a corner,
Pleading to be freed.

His shield could do with polishing,
The feather in his cap is moth-eaten.
But still he persistently cries for sovereignty,
Angry, he had finally been beaten.

His horse has its head bowed low,
It too has need of repair.
But the suit of armour still pleads on,
Falling deep into despair.

But no one ever hears him,
No on ever will.
But the suit of armour doesn't know this,
So he cries on still.

Mrinalini Dey

WHY DON'T LLAMAS . . . ?

Why don't llamas wear pyjamas
The same as you and me?
'Twould be the most ridiculous
Sight we would ever see.

But they'd be warm and snug at night,
They'd always wake refreshed and bright,
They'd wonder why they never wore
Such useful clothes in bed before;
And they could all wear diff'rent types,
With spots and checks and flowers and stripes,
In green and yellow, blue and red,
How smart they'd look asleep in bed.

So why don't llamas wear pyjamas
The same as me and you?
It's really very puzzling for
We all know zebras do.

Hilary J Cairns

A SWEET POEM

How lovely to see a lemon drop moon,
Adoring a blueberry sky in June.

Mountains of chocolate all dusted in white,
Pure sugar icing, thus making them bright.

Liquorice logs are the bark of the trees,
Angelica leaves that sway in the breeze.

Peppermint pebbles, a marshmallow shore,
Dolly mixture flowers, colours galore.

A cream soda lake and cranberry falls,
Little fudge houses with nut toffee walls.

Lollipop lampposts in soft treacle soil,
Sprinkled crushed peanuts, a sidewalk with style.

Imagine the fun to visit this land,
Confectionery Island. Why, it sounds grand.

Betty Hattersley

MY HAMSTER

My hamster's round and very fluffy
In fact people say he's rather scruffy
He runs round and round inside his wheel
It makes me want to laugh and squeal

Some may think it's very rude
To fill his pouches full of food

I let him run around the floor
But watch he doesn't run out the door
He's silky and so soft to touch
Looking after him doesn't take very much

Nicola Edis

THINGS THAT GO BUMP IN THE NIGHT

One night when I was very young,
I had an aching head;
I went into my father's room,
And this is what I said:

'Oh, wake up, Daddy; wake up please,
And stop that awful snoring.
It's given me a headache,
And what's more - it's very boring!'

I went down to the kitchen,
And brought back two wooden chairs;
You should have heard the clattering
As I threw them down the stairs.

My dad jumped up, and smacked my bum
With his big cricket bat.
Just then I woke up in a sweat -
D'you have bad dreams like that?

Roger Williams

THE WOODLAND WITCH OF HALLOWE'EN

A long time ago there lived a witch.
On her head a pointed hat,
She wore a long and tattered frock
Upon her lap a sleek black cat.

She rode forth on her broomstick
Every Hallowe'en.
She was the spookiest witch,
Ever to be seen.

In the woods you'd find her,
Making up her spells,
Leaning o'er her cauldron
Oh, those dreadful smells!

Six legs from a spider,
Stomach of a bat!
Worms and bugs, snails and slugs,
In that pot - so black.

See it steam and gurgle
'Abracadbra,' she'll screech with glee.
And when the mixture's ready,
She squats beneath the tree.

She stirs, she talks, she skips;
Then walks around the leafy glade
With mystic power, in just one hour,
Countless spells are made.

If you meet her don't feel scared
She'd never harm a child,
Even witches in their hearts
Are really kind and mild.

Pamela Carder

GRANNY

My friend Jimmy's granny is little, round and fat,
She keeps a small canary and a little tabby cat;
She smells of cloves and lavender, her wrinkled face is old,
And she knits him socks and jumpers to keep from the cold.

She cooks him cakes and biscuits, and yummy pasties too,
She takes him walking in the park, and sometimes to the zoo.
Her eyes are small and twinkly, her hair is frizzy grey,
We pop in on the way from school to see her every day.

I also have a granny but she's not like that at all,
Her hair is red and curly and she's sunburned, slim and tall;
She'll sometimes take me to the gym, we have a lot of fun,
Or we'll go roller skating - but we don't let on to Mum.

These days it seems that grannies are not all they're meant to be,
With a shawl about their shoulders and a cat upon their knee;
Or sitting by the fireside in a cottage in a wood,
Or handing out the sweeties - telling stories if you're good.

But whether old and wrinkly with hair of frizzy grey,
Or dieting and working out and keeping age at bay,
We like to have them spoil us, and to baby-sit for Mum;
Our grannies are a treasure and we love them, every one.

Ann Dempsey

MACKYE THE DWARF

In the days of old
When legends were told
Of dragons, knights and kings,
There lived a dwarf,
Under the wharf
Of the gypsy scenes.
His name was Mackye
As he'd only one eye
A gargoyle, she scratched it out.
He was small and green,
Hideous to be seen
And also very stout.

Said he one day,
'I'll go on my way
And find myself a bride.'
But everyone
Was quick to run
When he was espied.
So poor Mackye
With desperate cry
Said, 'It's sad to be alone,
Please come with me
And you will see
That I can make a friendly home.'

But others grinned,
'What live with him?
You'd have to be mad.'
Then they teased
Said as they pleased
And made that dwarf so sad.
As he went away
A maiden did say,
'I will live with you.
You dress smart
And have a good heart
This I know is true.'

Then in a flash
And almighty crash
Mackye was a shining knight,
And they spent their lives
As husband and wife in blissful pure delight.
The true beauty is not what's without
But what lies just within
If only you could take the courage
To take a close look in.

Kim Shea

MUM MISSED

Dirty doorstep at the front!
Dirty knocker on the door!
Dirty wellies in the hall!
Dirty footsteps on the floor!
Dirty saucepans on the stove!
Dirty tidemark round the bowl!
Dirty dishes in the sink!
Dirty towels, black as coal!

Dirt and grime is everywhere
In kitchen, lounge and hall -
And just to tread upon the stair
Lays a dust film over all!

But yesterday we had a letter,
And things will soon be right as rain -
For Gran, it said, is now quite better,
And Mum is coming home again!

Dan Pugh

LIONEL AND BESSIE

Lionel Lion and Bessie Baboon,
Fell in love one night in June.
They were so very much in tune,
And decided to marry pretty soon.

But Bessie fell down in a swoon,
After eating a poisoned prune.
Lionel jumped into a blue lagoon,
And roared for hours at the moon.

Rosemary Davies

DANNY DOWN THE DRAIN

Danny, the little dragon, had been given a holiday.
He'd finished all his work, been told to run away and play.
He set off from the castle gates and down the road he went
Not knowing then that night would be the worst he'd ever spent.
He came to Gertie's cottage where he smelt a lovely smell
Of lemonade and treacle. In fact it was a spell.
Gertie, the witch, had made it and left it there to cool
And Danny went and drank it, the silly little fool.
It made him start to shrink so he grew so very small,
That underneath a leaf you couldn't notice him at all.
The wind, it blew quite strongly and it began to rain
When he landed in the gutter, was washed quickly down a drain
And nobody could hear him when for help he tried to call
Because his voice became so thin and was so very small.
At first he swam and then he walked and soon it seemed to be
That he was getting bigger. Oh what calamity!
He found that he was growing back up to his proper size
And starting to breathe fire, so smoke kept getting in his eyes.
He kept on getting hiccups that were making such a noise
It woke up all the townsfolk and all the girls and boys.
At school on the next morning were allowed to try to see
If they could find what made the noise and solve the mystery.
At last, a girl called Sarah found out to her surprise
That staring at her from a grid, she saw two yellow eyes.
She called out to the others, 'Come over here and see
Whatever has two yellow eyes, as quick as you can be?'
'I think it is a dragon. What's he doing down the drain?
We'll have to get him out of here before it starts to rain.
He's grown back to his proper size. There isn't any doubt
We'll have to send for Gertie for a spell to get him out.'
She gave him more of grow-small spell, he climbed out of the drain.
Sir Whatsisname came up the street to take him home again.

Now Danny never goes alone outside the castle wall
Although he'd really like to, he never does at all.
The children sing a song about a dragon down a drain,
He only laughs and puffs out smoke and never does complain.

Margaret B Baguley

I AM SOMEBODY

We are all different, you and I
Uniquely created, I wonder why
Defining features and feelings too
Only one of me and only one of you

Dreams and desires and various goals
In accordance with each one of our souls
This is God's law, the way nature intended
Everyone's qualities so carefully blended

Learning from the mistakes that we make
Reconciling ourselves for our very own sake
Gladness, sadness, joy and woe
No one perfect, we are resilient though

Learning, developing, changing from birth
Discovering our value, our own self worth
Along life's road, whichever path we take
A journey to ourselves we are sure to make

We are strong, we are invincible
In truth a sheer miracle
Our very own body, heart and mind
Special, beautiful, one of a kind

We are all somebody, so be kind to yourself
Enjoy getting to know your vast inner wealth
So let us celebrate and shine like a star
Recognising just how important we all are!

Malvina Kovacs

A Mouse In The House

We have a new mouse
that's come to our house.
It can't run, it's not able,
it just sits on the table.

It doesn't eat cheese,
it's just here to please,
won't run down a hole,
be as shy as a mole.

It's no whiskers to twitch -
you just plug in a switch.
It's no tail to flick
but you can make it click.

And still with no tail
you can bring up e-mail.
You're never alone
when you plug in the phone.

I play with my mouse
all day in my house.

Helen Utting

PROFESSOR BUNSEN-BURNER

All first years! Heed this - be aware!
Take extra caution and extra care!
If there's just one teacher you should try to miss,
It's Bunsen-Burner, let me tell you this.

    As Bunsen-Burner's got x-ray eyes
    And Bunsen-Burner can read your mind
    Bunsen-Burner knows all your lies
    And Bunsen-Burner is never kind.

In his lab, late at night, he made a potion,
And he rubs it all over - like a cream or a lotion.
And it makes him invisible, so he's free as a bird,
To do what he wants without being heard.

    As Bunsen-Burner's got x-ray eyes
    And Bunsen-Burner can read your mind
    Bunsen-Burner knows all your lies
    And Bunsen-Burner is never kind.

There never has been such a horrible teacher,
He's only half human, half terrible creature
Who prowls and hunts when you're safe in your bed
Or are you? He could be an inch from your head!

    As Bunsen-Burner's got x-ray eyes
    And Bunsen-Burner can read your mind
    Bunsen-Burner knows all your lies
    And Bunsen-Burner is never kind.

So, first years, beware - keep your heads down low.
Don't give any clues about all that you know.
And if you get Bunsen-Burner for chemistry -
Hide in the cloakroom, here, next to me!

As Bunsen-Burner's got x-ray eyes
And Bunsen-Burner can read your mind
Bunsen-Burner knows all your lies
And Bunsen-Burner is never kind.

Andrew Detheridge

JACK RABBIT

I want to see my special friend
His name is Rabbit Jack
But I can't find him anywhere
I do hope he comes back
I've looked under mountains
And up the tallest tree
But I can't find him anywhere
Where can that rabbit be?
I thought I'd search the ocean
Or maybe check the moon
But Rabbit Jack just isn't there
I hope he comes back soon
I went to ask the owl
Who lives in tallest oak
But he was far too busy
Making oaka cola coke
He said to ask the badger
Who lives on Badger Hill
But when I knocked politely
I heard him shout, 'I'm ill!'
So off I went to search again
And walking through the woods
I saw a squirrel dancing
In a hat made out of mud
'Oh help me Mrs Squirrel,'
I cried with teary eyes
'I need to find my special friend
And you seem very wise.'
The squirrel, she stopped dancing
And removed her hat of mud
She said, 'I'm sorry little one
I'd help you if I could.'

She sent me to the sparrow
Who was sitting hatching eggs
She said she hadn't seen him
She'd been busy making pegs
Wherever could I find him?
Wherever could he be?
I even looked behind the clouds
And even inside me!
Then as the sky turned day to night
And quickly came the dawn
I remembered Rabbit Jack
Had not even been born!

Sarah Newell-Day

JASPER

Jasper my dog is such a pest
I try my hardest and do my best
But whenever I try to get him to sleep
I go up to bed and hear him weep.

I walk downstairs and go to his room
Walk past the mop and walk past the broom
Then what I do is get him to sleep
Go back to bed and have a good dream.

When I wake in the morning he's licking my nose
Licking my fingers and licking my toes
And when I'm eating my breakfast he's there at my feet
Waiting to get something to eat.

And when I'm at school he waits in the room
Hoping that I would be coming home soon
When I've come home he'll be stood at the gate
Waiting for me, his very best mate.

Danielle Beaumont (9)

FUNNY BONE

One day I found my funny bone
On my elbow, all alone
I found it quite by accident
Banged my elbow, 'Ouch,' I went
To me it all seemed very daft
For certainly, I could not laugh
In fact, it made me want to cry
I decided not to; don't know why
I've other bones all shapes and such
But they don't hurt me half as much
So you can stay all on your own
Not so funny, funny bone!

Janet Steele

MRS TIGGYWINKLE

Cleans her house every other day
Because it gets so dusty
She lives beneath the undergrowth
Where spiders, beetles, earwigs, slugs, live
Looking for grubs, whatever she can find
Scuttles home, dustpan and brush comes out
Shakes her prickly body
It's amazing what falls to the ground
She sweeps it up and throws all over herself
Two or three times, just for fun
She's so dusty, so dusty
You wonder if it was Mrs Tiggywinkle
But it was, so if you see a hedgehog on your garden
Think about Mrs Tiggywinkle
Who might wink at you
Passing through the dark night
She does you know
Dust does keep her clean and prosperous

Norma Flair Challis

DESCENT INTO THE MAELSTROM

The torrent rose. And swirled. And cast.
From deep within the Phoenix cackled,
Furious and fast.
Lurching forth. Faint hesitation.
Belching monumental incarnation.
From deep within the fury blasts,
It pallored - died,
The sea was calm at last.

Emily Grieves

VEGETARIANISM

My lady companion is a vegetarian true,
Often invites me to partake of her vegetarian stew.
Believe me, it really tasted fine,
I said, 'You are exceedingly kind,
Then she filled me up with her vegetarian wine.

On her television, there was nothing worth looking,
It was either 'Changing Rooms', or watching 'cooking',
A complete waste of time,
There was nothing on line,
So she filled me up with her elderflower wine.

We went for a picnic up Windermere, where,
The water was smooth and the sky very clear.
I thought the scenery was quite sublime,
'Let's go up the fells and have a good climb,'
But she brought out a bottle of her parsnip wine.

We go out in my car, 'tis something she enjoys,
We find a nice shady spot, away from the noise.
Rural beauty, 'tis nature's true design,
The fragrant breezes, perfect, sublime.
Then she produces a bottle of her rhubarb wine.

When my birthday came round, she gave me a treat,
Cauliflower and cheese and a nice quiche to eat.
With culinary skill, she really did shine,
Then she drank my health, in her dandelion wine.

When my life has come to an end and to Heaven I make,
There'll be St Peter, waiting at the Pearly Gate.
He'll greet me with a cheerful grin,
He'll open the gate to let me in,
'There's a stream over there,' he'll say. 'It's pure vegetable gin.'

Albert E Bird

THE SILLY WORD

'Boing,' said the apple,
'What a silly word to say,'
Said the little nodding daisy
As the apple bounced away,
'Apples should speak properly
Or sing a little song,
It's better not to speak at all
If all you say is, 'Boing.'

The wise old owl
Flew down to Earth
And to the daisy said
'Tell me please in just one word
I fell and hurt my head.'

'There's no such word,'
The daisy said
'As far as I have heard,'
'Precisely,' said the wise old owl
'So now it's not absurd
That after such a great big fall
The apple made the word.'

L Cottington

NOT A QUICK DELIVERY

Morning Sam how are you, deliveries going well,
All's fine to me there's no complaints, as far as I can tell,
I've got a letter in my bag that's been sent out to you,
I'll get it in a minute, in fact there's quite a few.
Some arrived last Wednesday but the address was hard to see,
It took a while to sort it out, so you can't blame that on me,
That's OK I said to Sam, I really understand, for I look forward
To my mail, the job you do is grand.

No time to chat must now get on, a lot of mail today, a lot of houses
I must reach no time for much delay,
Onward then he travelled, with a slow wave of his hand
And Mr Drake smiled to himself, a pile of letters in his hand,
Around the village he trudged on, a quick word here and there,
No time for idle gossip, he said to Mr Hare,
But the entire village understood a very busy man
And no one tried to slow him down, not that anybody can.

For he had been the postmaster, for years and he was good
And all had learnt to send their mail as early as they could
And every one had first class stamps; no second class was dared,
For that could take a fortnight, so all were well prepared,
To get their mail a few days late, they never took a chance,
So any special birthdays cards; they sent them in advance
And if you went on holiday you brought your postcards back,
'Twas quicker to deliver them, and stop and have a chat.

To tell them how the weather was, how the week had flown
And how you all enjoyed your stay, but it's good to be back home,
As for a special parcel, was sent with weeks to spare,
So you could then be certain, on time it would get there,
Mr Toad once waited a whole month, to get his pictures back,
Now he develops them himself, in his shed that sits out back,
The village all accept these things without a single wail,
For nobody would take the job, except our postman Sammy Snail.

K Townsley

TIMOTHY AND THE TIGER

Tiger. Tiger.
Please stay over there!
I really do not like -
The way you're sniffing the air!

Tiger. Tiger.
Please stay over there!
I really do not like -
Your sudden 'slitty-eyed' stare!

Tiger. Tiger.
Please stay over there!
I really do not like -
How your sharp claws can snare!

Tiger. Tiger.
Please stay over there!
I really do not like -
How your big teeth can tear!

Tiger. Tiger.
Not still over there!"
I really *do not* like -
Not knowing his where!

Tiger. Tiger.
Licking his lips! Back over there!
He really *does* like -
His fresh - Timothy - fayre!

Donna June Clift

GRANNY'S TREASURE CHEST

I went to visit Granny just the other day
Granny unlocked her treasure chest so that I could play
I lifted up the lid and got a big surprise
It really was a treasure chest - I couldn't believe my eyes
Glass beaded necklaces, bangles and rings
A yellow toy canary that you wind up and it sings
Tiny wax candles a game of solitaire
A very sad looking neglected teddy bear
I gave him a hug, which helped cheer him up
When I discovered an engraved silver cup
My granny's name upon it - for winning a race
She looked at me quite proudly, it showed in her face
Farmyard animals, horses, cows and sheep
A dolly with her eyes shut - in the chest asleep
An assortment of photographs all black and white
Chalks and a slate with which Granny used to write
A flower press with flowers - still intact
Perfume bottles and a powder compact
There was a penny and a halfpenny - three-penny bit
Why had she kept a puncture outfit
Recipe books from World War Two
Hand-written letters tied with a ribbon of blue
These are Granny's treasures collected over the years
Happy times, sad times - laughter and tears
I'm going to have a treasure chest so when I'm old and grey
I'll invite my grandchildren around - so that they can play.

Val Farrell

DOLLS

I saw her in the shop window,
Wooden stand hidden by her dress,
Peaches and cream complexion,
Clothes of purest silk no less.
Her eyes the colour of sapphires blue
Hair the gold of summer wheat,
Pearls around her throat and wrist
Glass slippers on her feet.

He stands beside her a soldier proud,
His uniform so grand,
Red and black with golden braid,
Sword held in his hand.
Feather plumes adorn his hat,
Black boots upon his feet,
His eyes the colour of night skies
Seem to smoulder with passion deep.

Looking at them standing there
I wonder if late at night,
When all the people have gone home
And the shop is shut up tight,
Does he put down his sword
Help her from her stand?
Then do they dance the night away
To a wind up music box band.

Mazard Mary Hunter

THE BIRDS

Blackbirds gather on the path
Venting on each other wrath.
Catching dew from tall black tulips
As you or I would sip mint juleps.

Robins build a cosy nest
They make it warm, with feathers dressed
And red geraniums are the blooms
That burn as bright as scarlet plumes.

A goldfinch settles on a branch
It looks for food, then takes a chance
On slugs or snails then turning up
When diving 'neath a buttercup.

A blue tit under fountain spray
Spangles in the sunshine ray.
It loves the water of its bath
Which spills out onto speedwell paths.

All the birds that visit here
On this garden shed a tear
For it's a place of love and hope
A temple of the heliotrope.

Hilary West

HALLOWE'EN - A POEM FOR CHILDREN

Lock all your doors and stay inside.
Creep into bed. Be sure to hide
From witches flying broomsticks that
Have at the helm a big, black cat.

With hectic hoots and high-pitched hollers
They change the stars to silver dollars,
Plundering coffers from the sky.
Why do they come? I'll tell you why.

From year to year these spectres sleep
In deathly hollows dank and deep.
They do not stir. They do not wake
And not a murmur do they make.

But when the cock crows on this day
They brush their cobwebbed eyes and say,
'We'll take a gun to shoot the sun
Then tell the moon it's time to come.'

Three witches stir a steaming pot
Of bubbling mixtures boiling hot.
They make a most disgusting stew
Of snakes and snails - a horrid brew!

Down in a dell by Badgers' Brook
In a secret, secluded nook
They chant their spells that can create
Double trouble for those they hate.

At last these demons of the night
Are hustled by dawn's fierce light.
Now that their wicked deeds are done,
They melt away like snow in sun.

Celia G Thomas

LUKE

He's only five, teacher's pet,
Smiled so sweetly when they met,
Forgets his book bag,
Says to Mum, 'Oh don't nag!'
Got first prize for his painting,
Won in the fancy dress,
Looked so charming, for five minutes,
Then exploded into a mess!

At breakfast in the morning,
He always spills his tea,
He waits till Mum's in the kitchen,
Then opens the door with the key,
Into the garden with clean school clothes
How he gets away with it,
Nobody knows!

Voice like an angel, eyes shine like stars,
Then he scoffs all my chocolate
And plays with his cars.
I'm sure, when he's grown up
He'll be good as gold,
As long as no one expects him . . .
To do as he's told!

Rose Childs

TEARS OF A CLOWN

Put on your mask to faced another day
While behind it you weep,
On the surface you seem happy enough
But you still cry yourself to sleep,

A broken heart is hard to mend,
But on the surface you just pretend,

You're trapped inside yourself alone,
With nowhere left to call your home,
No one there to hold your hand,
As once they said your life's been planned,

I look and look but cannot see,
The wonder's they say
Have touched me,

I remember Mummy's favourite food,
Being told off when I was rude,

When Daddy took me to the park,
And Basil when he played and barked,

But now I have nothing left
So I put on a mask to face the day,
Tears of a clown falling in May . . .
June, July, September, August and November
The mask is in front to all of you,
But behind the mask
I'm feeling blue;

Eamon John Healy

CHRISTMAS SPIRIT

It was cold outside and
nothing stirred upon the snowy ground.
The wind whistled through the trees,
naked they have been for many months now.

The days are short and
the nights seem to last forever.
All around me, people struggle
just to stay alive.

And then a ray of light
to cast away the darkness.
For Christmas cheer
is echoing throughout the land.

The little children expectant;
the old men reliving stories
from their youth, now long since passed,
as they huddle round an open fire.

And I, listening to all of this
and watching the outpouring
of joy, that this season brings
to all of our hearts.

David Watters

THE GLIBBASLOP

I have a tale that's bursting to tell,
About a creature that lives near a dell.
The Glibbaslop who's an ecological marvel,
Who on munch grunch days, travels to Kannarven.

Sometimes the Glibbaslop resides in a girhinosaurous grotto,
When fiendishly peckish for porridge with Bovril.
Oh! Its favourite nibbles I almost forgotto,
Mixed in a cauldron they bubble, frizzle and snorkel.

Pickled armadillo's toes sprinkled with rice,
Boiled badger, dipped in mustard and lice.
Curried toad stuffed with sage and bunions,
Roast bat, garnished with mint sauce and scorpions.
Slimy garden worms in tomato sauce served in a spicy beetle gravy.

And for dessert:
Maggot flavoured ice cream sprinkled with ants,
Or if he's feeling adventurous;
Rat crumble smothered in lashings of slug custard.

Delicious recipes? Some may jolly well agree,
I shouldn't want to have them for my tea.
Ugh!

Wasyl William Werezak

I DON'T LIKE PEAS

(Dedicated to my great grandson Riece Phillips who does not like peas)

I like to eat fish fingers be they English or Portuguese,
But one thing that I do not like is those things called peas,
Give me a pear or apple that grow on big, tall trees,
But don't you ever think of giving me those little peas.
I love the smell of bacon wafting to me on the breeze,
But I can tell you right now, I hate the smell of peas.
I will eat bread and jam or lovely sausages with ease,
But I can never get enjoyment from those small, green peas.
Cool ice cream now that I love or ginger pop that makes me sneeze,
But there is something that makes me feel ill, it is the sight of peas.
I love to eat crisps or sweets, I often crave my mum for these
But you know what you can do with your horrible peas.
So now you have the message, oh do say you have, please!
Promise you will never ask me to ever eat my peas,
I will ask you or even beg you, while I kneel on my knees,
Fill my plate with what you like but never give me peas.

Stan Gilbert

THE BEACH BALL

The ball rolled along the beach
Blown along by the gale
It began rolling towards the sea
And the little girl went pale

'Let it go,' her mother cried
'I will buy you another'
But the little girl wanted that ball
And shouted to her brother

'I'll get it for you sister dear
I can swim quite strong.'
'You're not to go, do you hear?'
'It won't take me very long.'

He then jumped into the ebbing tide
And swam towards the ball
It kept floating farther out
And the boy began to call

'Please help me it's too far out
I cannot swim anymore.'
The lifeboat crew were given a shout
For he was nearly at death's door

The boy was rescued from the sea
And taken safely to the shore
His sister turned to her mother and said;
'I don't want my ball anymore.'

It nearly cost her brother his life
And was a stupid thing to do
When his sister had given it thought
She said, 'My brother, I would rather have you.'

Violetta J Ferguson

THE TOY SHOP

The door closed and the key turned in the lock,
All went quiet then the toys became alive
Everything sparkled with light, as if a fairy had
touched them all with her wand.

Albert the Honey Bear yawned and stretched
his arms and feet
He climbed out of his basket where he'd laid
and toddled to the shop window and looked outside.
Soon he was followed by other toys,
Horace Hare, he was very fat
he had long floppy ears and feet.

'Let's have some fun,' said Hare.
'There's that big toy car
Come on Albert, let's try it out!'
Before Albert could stop him Hare was off,
climbed in the car and then got stuck.
'Oh no!' cried Albert, 'you silly old Hare.'

Albert placed a paw to his face, deep in thought,
'I know!' said Albert, 'we'll get a skipping rope.'
His big brown eyes searched around the shop,
'There's one right here, on the bottom shelf.'

Quickly the rope was tied around Hare's waist
And all the toys joined in with Albert taking
the strain on the rope.
'Pull! Pull!' said Albert, 'we've got to get him out,
Before the night is over or we'll be found out.'

They tugged and pulled but still he wouldn't move,
Albert sat down with paws to his head in despair.
When a tap on his shoulder caused him to stir,
It was Twinkle Toes, a white rabbit, all dressed in fairy clothes.

'Don't worry Albert, I'll get him out,
I'll wave my magic wand, and then he'll be out.'

And so it was Twinkle Toes Rabbit touched Hare
with her magic wand.
All became bright in the room with flashes of
bright magic dust -
And out stepped Hare, no worse for wear
to join the other toys again once more.

Albert yawned with relief, 'I am so tired.'
And climbed back into his basket and laid his head
down and went to sleep.
No sooner had he done this then all the toys
did the same and the shop became quiet once again.

Never the wiser of what had gone on,
The bright dawn sunshine shone through the
window, once more
Until a key turned in the lock to open
the shop once again.

Wendy McLean

THE CROCODILE

When I move I hear a rattle
And it isn't just my jaws,
Though they are in fact quite huge,
As indeed are my sharp claws.
It's all the stones down in my belly,
Grinding all my food to jelly,
With all the funny food I eat
I'd be feeling far from sweet,
Or even worse than that, I fear.
With nasty pains all coming near,
If I didn't have down in my tummy
All those stones you find so funny.

Joan Chapman

THE MOFFETS

The time has come to peek inside
The big green door, opening wide
A large oak table, six wooden chairs
A bright hallway leads to the stairs
Light trickles through a hole in the ceiling
Filling the hallway with a loving feeling
Six little mice tucked up tight
Saying prayers, wishing goodnight
Moffet mice sleep in two large beds
On woven flour sacks, resting their heads
Baby Moffets wrapped in a shawl
Fast asleep against the wall
So please sit down, enjoy with me
A tale of a windmill by the sea

A big fat fly flew round one day
He saw the windmill, and said, 'I'll stay!'
Baby Moffet sat under the tree
When the fly landed on her knee
She pushed it off with her hand
So it flew into the sand
Mandy Moffet played in the sand
Where the fly dare to land
Mandy flicked it with a spade
It flew to the grass where Molly was laid
Molly Moffet tried to splat
The big fat fly with her hat
It was too quick and flew away
I'm sure it will be back another day
Mum and Dad are glad to see
The fly has stopped bugging the family

Jane Clarkson

FRED

Fred, Fred go to bed
How many books is that you've read?
Funny books, mad books
Some very sad books
Don't you ever go to sleep?
In the middle of the night
At you, I peep
You're reading another book so deep
Slim books, fat books
Lots of cat books
Books everywhere
That everyone looks.

Susan Booth

THE PICNIC - A SPECIAL DAY

It was to be a special day
The grown-ups said it would
To let it hap, they cautioned me
To listen and be good.

But then the rain came down and stormed
Just at the break of day
It seemed to say, 'I'll spoil your fun.'
I'm here, yes, here to stay.

But no, we picnicked in the house
Upon my bedroom floor
With lemonade and jelly tots
And cookies by the score!

My mother raced me on all fours
My father was a bear
I laughed and ran outside the room
And scuttled down the stair

It sure has been a happy day
The grown-ups said it would
Despite the rain outside the house
The day was very good.

Jennifer Rene Daniel

DAYDREAM

As I walked through sun speckled trees, saw the summer sky
felt the sweet, warm breeze,
A bed of grass whispered, 'Come and lie and sleep beneath
my ocean sky,'
I wanted to walk on this beautiful day
but the tempting offer made me stay,
As the grass below swayed me soundly to sleep,
a golden bird in my dream began to peep.

'Hello!' he chirped and sang to me,
then he circled my head and flapped with glee,
He swooped and dived cos he wanted to play,
'Come on, get up, it's a beautiful day!
Then he screeched with fright, 'Quick fly with me,
the one-eyed cat's behind the tree.'
'I can't fly,' was my prompt reply.
So he flew away into the cloudless sky.

Out from behind a large oak tree, strolled
the one-eyed cat as fat as can be.
'My name is cunning cat,' he said, as he held
out his claws and bowed his head.
'I am a hunting cat, a clever cat, I like to catch birds,
I love to catch rats, this is how I spend my day,
then I lie and rest in the golden hay.'

Then out from behind a prickly bush, bounced
a three-legged dog in an awful rush.
'Cunning cat's fast, I always fail,'
he said puffing, panting and chasing his tail.
'I just like the chase, it's so much fun,'
he giddily said, then away he run.

With a drop of rain I awoke from my dream,
but had I really seen the things I had seen?
As I started to walk the long journey home,
I passed a three-legged dog with a juicy bone.
Then the most beautiful sound I had ever heard,
it must be the song of a golden bird.
Oh how I had, had the strangest day
but would I see a cat asleep in the hay?

Alison Garside

ZIG ZAG

Zig Zag the zebra
Fell in love with Debora
The giraffe,
Because she used to make him laugh.
Giraffes are very tall
Compared to zebras, very small,
But height doesn't matter
As they drank the Congo water.
Africa is very hot,
Helps if you're a Hottentot,
But it didn't stop the zebra or giraffe
As in the Zimzasi, they'd bath.
Perhaps you could ask them for their autograph!

Alan Pow

DEAR FATHER CHRISTMAS

Softly, silently, the snowflakes fall,
Sparkling silver, on rooftop and wall.
Timothy George is waiting to hear
The sound of sleigh bells, drawing near.

Mummy sent for the chimney sweep
So Father Christmas, his visit could keep,
For tonight is a very special time
When Father Christmas works overtime.

Timothy George peeps through the curtain;
Father Christmas is there, he's certain.
'Go to sleep now,' Mummy calls,
While outside the thick snow falls.

Last week Timothy George wrote a letter to say,
'Dear Father Christmas, with reindeers and sleigh.
I'll try to be good, for I know that I should,
So please call at my house on Christmas Day.
I would like a train-set, fishing rod and net,
Some sweets in a tin - and before I forget
A Boys' Own Annual, whip and top,
Some marbles and a toy sweet shop.

I will leave a mince pie and a drink for you,
Some carrots and water for your reindeer too.'
Softly, silently, the snowflakes fall
Sparkling silver, on rooftop and wall.

Joan Thompson

KEIKO THE DOMINO WHALE

Keiko the Whale was freed today
    And tears fell from my eyes
He slid into the deep black water
    Under northern skies
The water was icy
    Felt good on his skin
He was suddenly happy
    Now life could begin
He squealed with delight
    And diving deep
Overwhelmed with happiness
    He started to weep
His tears and mine are salty
    We're both tied to each other
He is like a kin of mine
    And I am like his mother
From hereon in he'll smell fresh air
    Where ocean breezes blow
I dream he'll reach the far horizons
    And to many places go
May every Animal be freed from bondage
    Freed from searing pain
It's what I want with all my heart
    So sings my heart's refrain
And so dear Keiko swim away
    Enjoy the open sea
Sing loud your song for all to hear
    But sing it specially for me

For Keiko . . . popularly known as Willy
Written the day he was partly released
Thursday 10 March, 1998 . . . Bon Voyage

Clare Marie Zeidrah Keirrissia Marshall

FRIENDS IN THE GARDEN

A little bunny came to my door
I gave him food
He wanted more
Then it was a little cat
Very, very thin
But now he's fat
A hedgehog and a tortoise
And a little turtle dove
All came to my door
All looking for love.

Marjory Gordon

IS THERE A MOUSE IN YOUR HOUSE?

Is there a mouse in your house?
There is in mine.
He comes out in early morning
Before the sun can shine.
Sits on the mat and winks at me
As I try to write poems in the dark.
Maybe he thinks he'll inspire me -
That would be rather a lark!

Is there a mouse in your house?
There is in mine.
When he thinks I'm not looking
He steals my cooking.
Sits on the mat and chews calmly away,
Not knowing or caring, what I might say!

Is there a mouse in your house?
There is in mine.
Last week he bit into some new-bought cheese
Sat on the mat completely at ease.
The week before, tore a hoover bag.
Took no notice of this old hag!

What to do with that kind of mouse
Making havoc in my kind of house?
Wait until he's taking a nap
Then put some bait in a great big trap!

Maureen Carr

POND SPRITE

My friend Yog is a frog,
He's just like ordinary folk except for the croak.
That's all he'll ever do for you.
Croak, croak! Yog hopped
into my life one winter's day
when I broke the ice on the pond.
Then like a cork out of a
champagne bottle, he flew forth from
the froth. Through the seasons
he gave good reasons for his birth
upon the earth. He would often
hold court with the newts
and would return their salutes.
But quite out of the blue, he did something
new, instead of a croak he spoke.

He spoke to me which filled me with glee.
He told me of his plan to gain an audience
with the Ant King - Zazing. I could come too
and we could use pond water to make a brew.
The rest as you know is history but
if you don't, let's keep it a mystery.
The ants always drive a hard bargain,
leaving no stone unturned. They've contracted
me to keep our meeting secret and the contract
had to been gone over with a fine ant.
A very fine ant, an import ant arrived
on a plant as part of a transplant.
Yog warned me that no one spawned the ants, not even him,
and if I didn't sign, things could get grim.
So better with the current swim, that is if I were fond of the pond
because frogs could croak. But let's not get jumpy,
nothing's happened yet, and nothing will, that's my bet.
What can the ants do to us? *Ouch!* It bit me!

Vann Scytere

HIS NAME . . . IT WAS JIM I THINK!

The moon was shining into my room. Curtains always open, to let in the
light . . . and also to allow darkest night to leave before the morning.
As I lay there in my bed, those different thoughts that crowd my head,
The ones that stop the dream-makers going off to work . . . silly
thoughts, leave me now I have to sleep . . . or try at least.

I could have been half asleep . . . maybe even half awake, when I heard
this sound. I don't think it was the dream-makers, nor people in the
street. Could it have been Mrs Warren's ginger cat . . . he was a one
for making a noise.

'Please be not afraid,' this little voice called to me. 'I was only after
some shelter and shade. A bite to eat and a drink.'
Fear was running wild inside my head as I tried hard to hide in my bed.
'Who are you?' I cried. 'I'll shout my mum and dad.'
'Forgive me for giving you a fright, allow me to put on my lantern
bright. You'll see, there's nothing to fear from me.'

The room was filled with a glowing light. There underneath was this
tiny person, in a striped blue coat. 'Greetings!' it said. 'My name is Jim
. . . Jim, I think!'
'Does that mean you're not sure your name is Jim?'
'No!' he said, most annoyed. 'I think it's what I do . . . that is my job.
I work in Father Christmas's factory.'

My heart jumped for joy. What a wonderful thing to happen to a boy,
I always believed, however much the others would laugh at me.
'So why are you here? Why come to me? It's only September, far too
early to put up a Christmas tree.'

There was some trouble in the land that's far away and I had forgotten
how to think. Father Christmas told me quite politely, 'Come along
Jim, this will not do there are new presents to be made . . . one's
thought of by you.'

I tried so hard but the thoughts had all gone . . . Mrs Christmas had the
answer, we hoped. 'Jim, you must go away, visit the children see what
their thoughts have to say.'

Me and Jim sat talking all the night. He said, 'Thank you Steven, you are my partner - my friend.' You will never guess what ideas we came up with! Well, on second thoughts, perhaps not. Wait till Christmas and you will see . . . *bye'*.

G J Cayzer

DIFFERENT FACE

Are you my dad who's just
Come back from the war?
Are you my dad that my mum
Has been waiting for?
Because she's given me this old photo
That looks like you, but
I'm not quite sure!

If you are my dad, but
I'll be ever so glad, to know
That you're my dad.

Oh yes! Oh yes! I'm ever so glad
That I'm the dad who you've been
Waiting for.

As it's that time that gave me this
Different face. But my feelings
For you are still in the right place.
And my love for you is still in my heart.
Do you know that I'm ever so glad
That you're *my dad!*

P Wilcox

To Katinka

Tinka, Tinka, Tinka, Puss, Puss, Puss, Kitty, Kitty, Kitty -
Each morning that would be my call, a daily pussy ditty.
Each morning I would let her out as soon as I was dressed,
She wouldn't wait for food or milk but darted out with zest.
For half an hour or so I'd see Katinka on the wall,
Or on the cats' club garage roofs, beloved of moggies all
She'd meet her friends, she'd chase a tail or pounce at butterflies;
She dearly loved her mornings out though blue or grey the skies.
And when it came to breakfast time, the neighbours knew my call
And saw my Tinka's smoke grey form, upon the gate or wall.
Into my arms she'd come and rub her head against my cheek;
A loved and loving friend was she, no better need you seek.
Tinka, Tinka, Tinka, Puss, Puss, Puss, Kitty, Kitty, Kitty -
The neighbours laughed but liked to hear my daily pussy ditty.

Kathleen M Hatton

TAKE AWAY

'Okay!' he said
'Who wants what?'

'Ten spring rolls'
Said the giant panda
While the lion debated
'A chicken pasanda'
'Lamb vindaloo'
Said the Bengal tiger
'I'll have one too!'
Said a hump-backed spider
'Cod and chips twice'
For two little penguins
'Barbecued ribs'
For the lazy lynx
'Pizza margerita'
For the turtle and the zebra
And they said it together
'Jinx!'

'Crispy duck'
Purred the sleek black cheetah
'Sausages in batter,' shouted the chimp
But the crocodile scowled
He just couldn't decide
Thrashed about angrily, trying to think

Then the crocodile smiled
'I'd like . . . that zebra!
Then for my main course, I'll have that gazelle
For pudding, I'd like
The chimp and the cheetah
And maybe I'll eat the keeper as well!'

'Huh!' said the python
When the order was done
(But he said it very quietly)
There's always one!

Nicolette Turner

An Enchanted Place

In that enchanted land,
Where first you held my hand
And the whole, wide world
Came out just to play.
There was poetry in the park
And dancing after dark,
And the band was playing in the square
Just because we both were there.
And that enchanted place
With all its beauty and its grace
Was where the two of us first learned to sing,
A song beyond the world's imagining.

Stewart Gordon

GILBERT OF SALISBURY

Gilbert lives
in the middle of town
On account of his size
he's easily found
At eight feet high
and five feet wide
He sits with a grin
to show off his pride
Everyone loves him
cute as a bear
You can't help but smile
when seeing him there
With pointed tail
and wings out spread
Red and green
from toe to head
A creature of fancy
made all of plants
When we are asleep
he's likely to dance
Floating like magic
his feet off the ground
From street to street
they move him around
Have you guessed what he is yet?
I'll give you a clue
The smoke from his nostrils
is probably blue
Of course! He's a Dragon
as everyone knows
The mystery is
where next will he go?

Deborah Hall

THE PET

We had a rabbit, a little white rabbit
She would run across the lawn, it was her daily habit.
Her eyes were very pink and her hair the softest fluff
And her tail a little ball, like a snowy powder puff.

The children really loved her, she was their favourite pet
They would hunt food for her, as much as they could get.
But her waist seemed to suffer and I fear she got *rather* fat.

Till one day, four baby bunnies appeared upon our mat,
We'll have to hunt for lettuce and carrots and lots of other things
The kiddies all did say,
'Please Mum, we'll look after them don't give them away!'

Dad had to make an effort and build a great big hutch
They were lovely little things to cuddle, stroke and touch
Mum said, 'They'd be good at maths, particularly multiplication!'
She said, 'All rabbits worked hard for the rabbit population.'

We didn't really understand when we went off to school,
But thought, they might help us with our prep; and that would
be real cool!

Jacqueline Bartlett

JACK THE FARMER

There was a farmer called Jack,
And he had an old tattered sack,
He nailed it to some bits of wood
And made a scarecrow best he could!
Now when he went to bed at night,
The scarecrow's eyes flickered with sight,
The scarecrow began to walk along,
Others came and joined the throng.
'Now look here, you lot,' said a scarecrow,
'We want some money, this is a poor show,
They expect us to stand around all day,
Bored to tears without any pay!'
So they went and woke poor Jack,
'We want pay, a pension, four weeks holiday a year,
And at least bring us the odd pint of beer!'
They pestered poor, bewildered Jack,
He'll be more careful with his old sacks!

Lorraine Green

FAIRIES AT THE BOTTOM OF THE GARDEN
(All about Fairy God Borivana, his Fairyland and his Fairies)

Borivana, the Fairy God, woke up and there was blackness all around him. *I don't like this!* he thought.

'Bring me light
Bring me light
To ease my sight.'

'Whoosh!' A bright blue sky appeared above him with rays of yellow light radiating from a large round orange sun. He lay back enjoying the light and the warmth - and it was day!

After some time, Borivana became tired and wanted to sleep again - but it was too light. So he said -

'Bring me night
Bring me night
And take the light!'

'Whoosh!' Darkness reappeared, but this time lit gently by many twinkling stars and a soft yellow moon - and it was night!

Borivana awoke to a beautiful sunrise but he was very thirsty.
So he said -

'Bring me rain, the very first
Because I need to quench my thirst.'

'Whoosh!' Black clouds appeared above him and rain poured down all around him and Borivana quenched his thirst.

It continued to rain and rain until rivers and great seas were formed and the land was pushed up in between. The rain and the sun made grass appear and then fruit, flowers and trees -and he called all this Fairyland.

It is too empty, thought Borivana, so he mixed some of the soil with the rain and

'Whoosh!' with his clay he made many fairy fishes to swim in the rivers and the seas and many fairy birds to fly in the air and many fairy animals to walk on the land. He named each and everyone of them.

Then Borivana thought, *I must make something very special, something very clever and caring who will look after this wonderful Fairyland that I have created.* So he mixed some very special clay and -

'Whoosh!' He'd made many fairies - the fruit and flower fairies with their gossamer wings and pretty garments in lavender, pink, blue and yellow. He made the mining fairies who work tirelessly mining the fairy dust that all fairies need to sprinkle, to be able to perform their magic spells. He made Daddy and Mummy fairies, little boy fairies and little girl fairies. He made the tooth fairies who take away any teeth that the child fairies leave under their pillows replacing them with presents.

Borivana was very happy with the beautiful Fairyland that he had created and with all the beautiful fairies that he had put in it.

But there is a secret that I would like to share with you. You see some of these fairies fly away from Fairyland and come to visit our world.

Look very carefully for the grassy fairy rings which fairies have made to guide other fairies so that they will know exactly where to land.

There are many tooth fairies who visit our children and take the teeth from under their pillows and leave them presents in their stead.

The Sandman, who puts magic sand in our eyes to make us sleep is also a fairy. there are flower fairies and many, many others.

You may be one of the very lucky ones, so look carefully as you may have *fairies at the bottom of your garden!*

E Marcia Higgins

ON THE BEACH

Steve and Stella spread their towels on sand
hoping very soon to look fit and tanned.

As they sunbathed there, relaxed and lazy,
everything grew vague and heat-hazy.

Later, when they woke, sat up, looked around,
a much more agitated beach they found.

They saw seaweed in a pool, start to shake,
creatures inside shell, very wide awake

and frightened. On rock, as keenly aware,
limpets and mussels, till then fastened there,
tried to prise themselves away from danger.

And overhead, what was even stranger,
all seagulls stopped swooping and fell silent.
In all directions flying off they went . . .
though on the sand crabs were scuttling about,
other creatures too, running in and out . . .

Then Steve and Stella both leapt to their feet,
each conscious of a much quickened heartbeat
for, slowly emerging out of the sea,
an enormous Sea Beast they could both see.

Though vast and slimy, its shape it could change -
they needed to get themselves out of range.

They raced to the cliff, clambered to the top
while down on the beach that Blob did not stop
from grabbing and gobbling all that it found
running above or hiding underground.

Flabbergasted, they saw tentacles snatch
their towels, its eyes examine their catch . . .

It waved their towels at them as it sped
triumphantly back to its ocean-bed.

Chris Creedon

THE PINK AND YELLOW PONY

The pink and yellow pony
Went down to the sea
He played among the rock pools
And had seaweed for his tea
He frolicked in the ocean
And got lobsters in his mane
The pink and yellow pony
Never went there again

Bill Peters

THE ONCOMING TIDE

We'll build a boat on the beach today,
We'll make it strong as we face the sea.
The walls of sand will be high and wide
To face the waves of the oncoming tide.
We'll stand in our boat as we build up the sides
Watching the sea as the tide comes in.

The sides seem secure as the water laps nearer
Right round the back of our little boat.
How long can it last as the tide comes in?
We'll repair the front as the water flows over -
Quickly with spades more sand must be found.
Faster we dig to build up the sides - but,
All too soon our boat is submerged by the sea,
We lost our boat to the oncoming tide.

Shirley Burgon

THE GOOD LIFE

I'd like to be a leopard, sleeping in a tree
And only have to rouse myself when it was time for tea
With legs and tail all drooping down
I'd be a wondrous sight
I'd wrap around the branches,
And sleep all through the night

And when the antelopes came by
I'd stir and take a chance
To have one for my breakfast,
In the fast food restaurant
With such a carefree life as this
Without a fret or care
I'd swap it for the busy life
I have in Aberdare

Wesley Stephens

TWO BY TWO

Up the long neck of a kangaroo
Climbed a swarm of ants two by two
And when they finally reached his ear
Two by two they'd disappear
What a nice home they thought, this ear
No one to bother us so high up here
But the kangaroo wasn't too pleased with this
So he twitched his head and gave such a hiss
That the ants they twisted and finally fell
Inside his neck down a long dark well
Until at last they hit the bottom
And two by two digested, forgotten

John Wayre

Unicorn Of Shangri-La!

Proud and erect stood he - a thoroughbred
One of great bearing and nobility true,
So poignant a scene as revealed to me
The natural cousin of Pegasus - in view.
But was it true reality - or just a dream
Stirred by some inner emotion reborn,
The vision so vivid - surreally experienced
To see my mystically becalming - unicorn.

'Twas far off, in a distant paradoxical land
Full of colours angelic, ingenious - contrite,
Where I gazed full of amazement, emotions sublime
As I travelled so tirelessly - beckoned that night.
This fabulous and gracious creature to behold
Surrounded by a pastel mist - stood he so white,
Radiating peace and tranquillity by presence
Mellowing dark moods, unjust causes - put to plight.

Periwinkle embossed yet - straight angled horn
Surmounting his long crinkled trailing main hairs,
Belied by his angelic, calming face - siren
With its none frightening, beguiling stares.
Guardian as bequeathed by Mother Nature herself
To this a land of untainted redress,
True Shangri-La, as often denoted in myth
Final resting place of uncomplicated, complete happiness.

Gary J Finlay

ON REFLECTION

Do you remember when you were small
Your favourite story of them all
That you asked to be read every night?
Well mine was the story of 'Snow White'
With seven dwarfs and a wicked queen
But every night? Made my mother scream
So she devised a game to keep me amused
With my own children, it's a game I've used
My sister was Mary, my name Irene
And with a mirror, she set the scene
'Mirror, mirror on the wall
Who is the fairest of them all?
Our Mary has a face serene
But the fairest one is our Irene'.
But not every verse was full of praise
It depended on good and naughty days
Then my mother would make me pay
For the naughty things I'd done that day
Like 'Mirror, mirror on the wall
Who is the fairest of them all?
Well, Irene's cross and acting funny
For the fairest of them all is Mummy'.
Or 'Irene's face is really scary
The fairest one is little Mary'.
Of course we all collapsed in laughter
But I loved 'Snow White' forever after.

June Davies

FAIRY RING

Let's all go and find a fairy ring,
Where fairies at night, dance and sing.
Blades of grass are trod flat to the ground,
Where fairies dance when there's no one around.
They laugh, they dance, they sing,
And all hold hands in a ring.
Each one's dressed in different flowers,
And to make it took them many hours.
Right through until morning they will be there,
For what life holds, they need not care.
Each ring holds their magic, it is quite true,
Each ring is for wishing, and believe if you do,
That every wish made will come back to you.

Denise Clegg

THE BUZZZZZ WORLD

The many worlds we pass by are so diverse and complex
The creatures we swat at and cry away from
Are only going about their lives like you and I
The portly, fuzzy buzzy bees
Laden from head to legs in pollen
The jovial gentlemen, dancing inside each flower
Gracefully tumbling around like a breakdancer
The skylarks are their backing group
'Hey, get with the beat Bee Bee'
A tall, elegant fly with the very long nose
Gracefully on long legs, dips her proboscis into nectar-filled cups
Whilst - the poacher alias Spy Spider
Lays a silken trap for to catch a fly
Then lets himself down on a silken abseil and wraps in a silk cocoon
Lunch for tomorrow me thinks
Bearing weight double his size, drags it back to his lair
And hangs in it his larder
The very correct hover fly, so smart and clean in striped suit
Washes each dip into a flower with versatile legs, so particular
His enormous, faceted eyes looking and looking around
Whilst bluebottles crowd the food bars in their blue iridescent suits
The wise boys of the city
Buzzing loudly into their mobile phones
Doing lucrative deals on nectar on the net
I hope they don't go too near *the web!*

Hilary Jean Clark

BLUE DOLPHIN

In the deep blue sea
there lived a dolphin called Blue.
He was a big, strong and friendly, lively chap
who did lots of tricks on his back
and especially when you did clap.
He delighted in entertaining to be
because he was oh so sweet and clever
not forgetting friendly.
I had to go on a boat
just to visit him at his home
the deep ocean sea.
This is why I call him Blue,
he's special see.

Sharon Blossom Brown

MILK TEETH

Dear John,
I've just bitten into my bun,
Yesterday,
I had two teeth.
But today,
There's only one . . .

Margarette Phillips

FROG TALK

In my garden one wet day,
I moved a stone and there he lay.
A big green frog
All slimy and wet,
As ugly as a frog could get.
I looked at him for quite a while,
He looked at me and seemed to smile
'Ribbitt, ribbitt,' he said to me
But I didn't understand. You see,
I can't talk like a frog can talk.

Andrew Whittingham

AN ENGINE CALLED PUFF

There was a railway engine called 'Puff'
Who always moaned he'd had enough,
He was driven from London to Leeds,
At very fast and very slow speeds,
When hungry he ate lots of fuel,
And thought the passengers were cruel;
Why did they complain if he was late?
Didn't they know he also carried freight?
Sometimes he was shunted up and down
On the outskirts of a noisy town,
And this made him puff and puff and pant,
Which didn't make him feel very gallant;
One day the track was electrified,
And sadly he became mummified;
He no longer sped through hills and dales
But was left for dead upon the rails.

Eric Allday

GREEN HAIRY MONSTER

It's magical, mystical, chilling and scary.
It's green and it's lumpy and monstrously hairy.
It lives in a cupboard or under the bed
And it comes out at night with its eyes shining red.

It's savage and cross, with a terrible frown
And it climbs up the curtains and hangs upside down,
Then it drops to the floor and it lands on its head
And then lies on the carpet pretending it's dead.

Then up it will leap with a frightening screech
To smash any furniture left within reach.
It's hoping that I will be getting the blame
For the things that get broken. It's always the same
With a monster like this. For they're cunning and sly
And will not attempt to look *me* in the eye.
So I know that it's wicked, I know that it's bad
And very ferocious and just slightly mad.

But I'm not afraid of a monster like that.
I tell it to go and command it to scat
And then it will disappear, just like a mist,
Cos I made it all up!
    So it doesn't exist!
                Phew!

John Foster-Turner

EXCUSES FOR FORGETTING YOUR HOMEWORK

'Tony, where is your homework?'
'The dog ate it, Miss!'

'Now Tony, really where is your homework?'
'Well, I was at my gran's,
I was doing it, but the triple-eyed, green-footed,
Cyber-toothed monster ate it.'

'Tony, where is your homework?'

'I forgot it, Miss.'

Laura Fisk

You Don't Scare Me

Someone is following in my footsteps
Someone is walking close behind
Is there really someone there
Or is it only in my mind?

Someone is in my bedroom
I feel a presence with me
Someone is standing by my bed
But the more I stare the less I see

Someone follows me about the house
As I go from room to room
Is that just the wind I hear
Or are they whistling a tune?

If someone is following me
What I would like to know the most
Is will they ever speak to me?
For I'm not afraid of ghosts

To someone who is following me
Reveal yourself if you must
For I would like to stay and talk to you
But you probably won't see me for dust

A Wilcox

HALLOWE'EN

It's Hallowe'en, the spooks are out,
With the noises and the cackles all about,
Everyone's out,

It's Hallowe'en, the vamps are out,
Witches brewing spells are all about,
Everyone's out,

It's Hallowe'en, the ghosts are out,
Ghouls and monsters creeping all about,
Everyone's out,

It's Hallowe'en, the sweets are out,
All the little children dance about,
Everyone's out,

Won't you come out?
Please come out,
Trick or treat,
Hallowe'en's *neat!*

Jacqueline Donnelly

BEWITCHING

The witch is evil,
As evil as can be,
As evil as the darkness set free.

She has a long nose,
And a very long chin.

She rides on her broomstick,
In the dark sky,
Her cat miaowing
Aloud at the back.

You'd think it a nightmare,
If you heard her laugh.

D S Edwards

KIDS

Finger marks on all the doors.
Children playing on all fours.
Grandma smiling happily
Four kids have come to tea.
Busy hands making things
Oh what joy children bring.
How time goes quickly by
Having fun, sometimes they cry.
Soon it's over, time to go.
Homeward bound, here we go.
Back to Mammy, tired eyes.
Lots of kisses, hugs, goodbyes.

Edie Glen

WIGGLY WORM

Oh wiggly worm
Lying on my stair
Surely you must be frozen
With no clothes to wear

Oh wiggly worm
Why don't you come along
Join us in my warm house
And sing us all a song

Oh wiggly worm
You sang so splen-did-lee
In fact you sang so very well
Why don't you stay for tea?

Andrew Younger

THE SCARECROW

Walking through fields on a hot summer's day
I saw a scarecrow amongst all the hay
He said, 'Come here boy and take my hand
You're going on a journey to Scarecrow Land.'

We walked hand in hand over meadow and stream
To a place I'm sure no one had ever seen
There was music and singing, laughter and wine
Where dozens of scarecrows were having a good time.

They give the impression of standing still
How they're placed in fields at random, at will
Dressed in old clothes with sticks and straw
But come alive they do as I once saw.

They're only scarecrows, nothing more, nothing less
But I know different, and if I were to guess
Under their disguise we all can see
Sometimes they're not what they appear to be.

Keith Helliwell

HE SAID HIS NAME WAS PARAWACK

A coal-black cat crossed my path,
Long-whiskered and golden-eyed.
He sat down, pausing for a chat,
Offering not a single miaow,
For he spoke in purrfect English.
And when I asked his name,
He said, 'My kitfolk call me Parawack.
A traditional family name,' he replied.
'It has run in my family for a thousand years.'
At that time it seemed to please him
For loudly he began to purr,
As about my feet he curled
Lying undisturbed for some moments,
Then began earnestly to lick his sleek fur.
I offered him some milk in a china dish.
Though he declined my sardine fish,
Saying, 'I am a fine feline prince,
And I dine only on those of gold.
I have many ponds of them at home,
Where I recline on no mundane chair,
But on a high and stately throne.'
Of course, I should have known.
His line arose in the time of Pharaohs.
Did not his forebears wear a fine collar,
Made of soft leather, gold and emeralds?
At that point the air around him trembled.
As he vanished from my sight,
That is but for his golden eyes,
And his warm Cheshire cat smile,
Which too, faded after a while.

Jonathan Pegg

HOLIDAY

Hooray, hooray
for tomorrow we're off on our holiday.

We're going to the seaside
where the seagulls fly high
where the crabs crawl sideways
and giant ships sail by.

There'll be toffee apples and candyfloss
as much as we can eat
we can run along the beach
with the sand between our feet.

Then I'll buy a postcard
to send to my friend, Heather
telling her of all the fun
and some lines about the weather.

As soon as I get there
I'll buy a silly hat
one of those 'kiss me quick' ones
what do you think of that?

Catherine Watson

MARTIN THE MONKEY

Martin the monkey climbed up a tree
Sat upon the highest branch to see what he could see
There was Mrs Lion basking in the sun
Her little cubs were playing, having lots of fun
Giraffes were stretching up their necks
As long as they could be
Reaching for the berries hanging on the tree
Far away the elephants walked in a line
The baby one was keeping up, doing really fine
And when he saw his monkey friends
Having lots of fun
He scrambled off to join them
As fast as he could run

Gloria Aldred Knighting

UNTITLED

One little bird sits in a tree
He sings a song for you and me.

Two little puppies, small and sweet
Loads of kisses when we meet.

Three little fishes swimming about
Pussy is near so do watch out.

Four little kittens on a wall
Who is prettiest of them all?

Five pink mice so very sweet
Made of sugar for us to eat.

Six little piglets in a sty
With Mummy and Daddy pig standing by.

Seven little ducklings go swimming by
Eating bread from children nearby.

Eight little lambs so frisky yet shy
Running to Mummy sheep as we pass by.

Nine little chicks with mother hen
Another comes running and then there are *ten*.

E Timmins

FILMING

Went filming just the other day
as an extra in an ad
non-speaking part I do admit
(my bark is not that bad!) . . .

They fussed and petted me ad lib
'twas quite a pleasant time
walked on and off at each request
in a long but easy mime . . .

The time stars took to get it right
while I lounged around at will!
Next time I'll get a speaking part
maybe on the 'Old Bill' . . .

I won't say I'm a show-off but
next time the ads are shown
I'll not say no to some applause
now that my cover's blown . . .

Margarette L Damsell

MELLOW THE BEAR

Mellow's the bear on the clock,
With the time he will rock.
He just rocks around all night,
No one ever puts him right.
Sometimes he's put in the hall,
On a fixture in the wall.
He can't stand on a shelf,
He likes to hang by himself.
On any fixture he'll rock,
To the movement of his tick-tock.
He has a special friend near,
A miniature toy teddy bear.
When in the window the sun starts to creep,
He'll soon wake you from your sleep.
He gives you time so you don't fuss,
When you're in a hurry to catch the bus.
Steady he rocks to and fro,
Hurry up, it's time for you to go.

Margaret Upson

TOMMY'S BROTHER
(My little man, Tommy)

Little Tommy's brother, Tim
Was too small to play
When he grows
I shall choose
A game
Yes, I can't lose
Mummy said be some time
For you're five
And in one's prime

Michael D Bedford

HARRY'S LEFT

Harry Who hadn't a clue
To where his folks had gone
All he got was a note
Saying, 'Harry, so-a-long'.

Harry Who is left behind
His folks have gone away
'I'll go to my sister's
There, for me to stay.'

Harry Who's sister's gone
So Harry's on his own
'I'll go to the pictures
Then I won't be alone.'

Harry Who finds the cinema closed
What's he going to do?
Oh poor wee Harry
Doesn't have a clue.

Harry Who, he wakes up
It was all a dream
And wee Harry knows
His family are not that mean.

J Lanigan

DOZY, DIPPY AND DIZZY

Dozy the dinosaur got her name
Because she was no good at games
To see her friends go racing by
Made poor Dozy want to cry
She could not run or skip or jump
She just went waddle, thump and flump.

Dizzy the dinosaur's neck was long
But her stomach was not strong
Reaching up high gave her a fright
Because she was afraid of heights
A long-necked dino she may be
But Dizzy could not climb a tree.

Now Dippy the dinosaur had wings
She could fly and land on things
To build a nest took lots of space
So to a large rock she would race
There she would sit to hatch her eggs
Then teach her young ones to use their legs.

Joan Gallen

ZEB BEAT

A zany zealous zebra
from distant Zanzibar
sang a dotty little ditty
to his friends both near and far:

'Come and join my sing-along
with trumpets, drum, guitar
and have a giant swing-along
from an anthill to a star.'

So the elephants stampeded
with trumpetings bizarre
and rhinos splashed and snorted
while the monkeys squealed, 'Hurrah!'

The big cats drummed on tree trunks
and miaowed with claws ajar
while herds of hooves made rhythm
and thumped to a reed guitar.

The noise was so tremendous
with raucous cockatoos
that it scared the snakes to scarper
and was heard in Timbuktu.

Rosemary Keith

A WOODLAND FEAST

The table was made out of toadstool,
It was set for a sparkling lunch.
The buttercup wine was yellow and cool,
Stood next to the dandelion punch.

A dock leaf was used for a tablecloth,
Each cup from a daffodil head.
Nettles and thorns were mixed to make broth,
To go with the poppy seed bread.

The ant tucked into his piping hot dish,
Of daisy and mashed peppercorn.
Mr Bee was so pleased, he'd been granted his wish,
To dance with the fly on the lawn.

Everyone cheered to see the huge cake,
Wheeled in by the pleased looking lark.
They each took a slice and sat by the lake,
Where the frog sang until it was dark.

Nicola Cobham

FAIRIES

There's fairies at the bottom of our garden
I see them every day
Beautiful, delicate wings
Flitting as they play
Wings that shimmer in the sunshine
Silver and gold like gossamer thread
Tiny fairy footsteps
Leaving imprints on the ground

There's fairies at the bottom of our garden
They make no noise at all
In and out of flower beds
Watching leaves and petals fall
Playing leapfrog over toadstools
Chasing bees and flies
Spreading trails of fairy dust that nobody can see

There's fairies at the bottom of our garden
That only I can see
Grown-ups say there's no such thing
But they wave at me
They wear the prettiest dresses
Have lovely long blonde hair
It's a pity you can't see them
So you will have to dream

Lynn Toogood

SANDCASTLES

We went on a day trip
Mum, Dad and me
A whole day together
Playing in the sand and sea

Dad and I built a sandcastle
Where the sand was wet
Down near the sea's edge
The sand pies really set!

Dad sculptured impressive turrets
While I dug out a moat
We decorated it with flags
And I sailed my little boat

But suddenly the tide changed
Came in at quite a pace
Our lovely sandcastle was
Washed away in its wake!

It made me feel very sad
To see it washed away
But Dad said, 'It's only nature
That the tide turns twice a day!'

So to make up for my disappointment
Mum suggested we have a treat
'How about fish and chips
Eaten in a café, not in the street!'

On the long journey home
I fell asleep and dreamed
About a boy who lived in a sandcastle
And the tide never turned *it seemed!*

Heather Denham

ALIENS

A liens live in the universe
L ions live in the zoo
I n a kennel dogs will sleep
E ndings will be found in books
N umbers go like this, 1, 2, 3
S econds tick away throughout the day.

Helen C M Cowen (6)

THAT GNAT

Oh! What goes on in your little gnat's mind
    As you dance away under the trees?
        Whoopee! Bump!
You flit along carelessly, not looking behind,
    And you neither say pardon nor please!

In the shadows now, the light is just dying,
    As up, down, and around, you skim;
Sheer ecstatic delight in the joy of flying
    Since acrobatics help you to slim.

You don't make honey, seem to have no fears,
    But you bite in the night, I am told;
A low-level attack, whining by anyone's ears,
    To keep your little gnat's feet from the cold.

A gnat is musical, as I have espied,
    Quite high whines from a low scale gnat;
But that was when sharp-eared Moth replied,
    'Wake up! Wasn't that scatty gnat flat?'

If you don't do harm, do you do any good?
    You're there in a strange scheme of things.
You maybe food for the bats, that's quite understood,
    So freefall, as you snap shut your wings!

Up and around in your wild, giddy flight,
    You must drive all your cloud simply spare!
        Whoopee! Bump!
You are out there cavorting until almost night,
    As you came from nowhere, so now, go back there!

Dennis Marshall

A PARROT IN PASSING

I saw a purple parrot
Sitting on its perch,
Dozing in the sunshine
Just inside the church.

When the church bell rang
With a deafening clang,
The parrot jumped sky high.

With great eyeballs aloof,
His beak stuck in the roof,
And his proud feathers flew
Down into the pew.

'That's the way to do it,'
The preacher man cried.
'Amen,' said the parrot,
And he hung there and died.

A choirboy looking up
With a gentle sigh,
Got a dollop of bird dung
In his right eye.

'You've been blessed,'
Squawked the preacher man
As he knelt by the perch.
Then he picked up a peanut
And flew out of the church.

Bernard Brady

MOTHER KNEW BEST

'Don't go outside,' his mother said
'If the cat catches you, then you'll surely be dead.'
But Ferdinand Mouse thought that he knew best
And went out in the garden without any stress.

He wandered around under bushes and trees
Then suddenly he was pushed to his knees.
And there in the moonlight - a terrible sight.
The cat sat there grinning - oh dear, what a plight.

Cat unsheathed his claws with a gleam in his eye
And said, 'Hello Ferdie, I'm afraid it's goodbye.'
He clawed poor Ferdie and made him bleed.
He was a frightened mouse indeed.

Ferdie tried to run but his legs were unsure.
The cat just laughed and came back for more.
Soon Ferdie was battered and bleeding profusely.
He thought of his mother's words somewhat morosely.

If only he'd listened. He'd been such a fool.
At the time he thought he'd been acting so cool.
And so as he went to his final rest
He acknowledged the fact that *Mother knew best*.

His mother and sister searched for him next day.
But all that they found was his tail in some hay.
So weeping and wailing they returned to their nest
Knowing Ferdie now realised that *Mother knew best*.

Jennie Rippon

ANCHOR BOOKS
SUBMISSIONS INVITED
SOMETHING FOR EVERYONE

ANCHOR BOOKS GEN - Any subject, light-hearted clean fun, nothing unprintable please.

THE OPPOSITE SEX - Have your say on the opposite gender. Do they drive you mad or can we co-exist in harmony?

THE NATURAL WORLD - Are we destroying the world around us? What should we do to preserve the beauty and the future of our planet - you decide!

All poems no longer than 30 lines.
Always welcome! No fee!
Plus cash prizes to be won!

Mark your envelope (eg *The Natural World*)
And send to:
Anchor Books
Remus House, Coltsfoot Drive
Peterborough, PE2 9JX

OVER £10,000 IN POETRY PRIZES TO BE WON!

Send an SAE for details on our latest competition!